Sharky and

by Jan Burchett and Sara
Illustrated by Duc Nguyen

Say the sounds.

/ar/	ar *as in arm*
/or/	or *as in fork*
/ur/	ur *as in purse*

Blend the sounds to read the words.

sharp	lurks	torn
turns	short	dark

Sharky is hunting for food.

She lurks in the dark. She sees Floss.

Yum!

Sharky feels a sharp pain. Her tooth hurts.

Floss sees the tooth. It has a short weed stuck in it.

Floss tugs at the weed.
She tugs and tugs again.

Pop!

Sharky is happy. Her tooth is not hurting.

Sharky will thank Floss. She swims up to her.

I will be a shark snack!

Floss turns and darts off.

Sharky looks for Floss. She looks in the boat.

Sharky sees Floss in the weeds.

Thank you, Floss.

But Floss is in a net. It is hurting her.

Sharky has sharp teeth. She rips the net for Floss.

Floss bursts from the torn net!

Sharky and Floss are happy again.
They swim off to have fun.

Talk together

1. Why is Sharky's tooth hurting?

2. How does Floss help Sharky?

3. Point to the words with the **ar** sound.

shark   short   weed   sharp